The Art of the Journal

Reflections on Writing, with Space
for Original Observations

Running Press
PHILADELPHIA · LONDON

Canadian representatives: General Publishing Co., Ltd.,
30 Lesmill Road, Don Mills, Ontario M3B 2T6.

ISBN 1-56138-464-X

Cover and interior design by Lili Schwartz
Cover illustration by M. A. Lloyd
Interior illustration by Cynthia Carrozza
Edited by Brian Perrin
Typography: Futura by Deborah Lugar
Printed in the United States

This book may be ordered by mail from the publisher.
Please add $2.50 for postage and handling.
But try your bookstore first!

Running Press Book Publishers
125 South Twenty-second Street
Philadelphia, Pennsylvania 19103-4399

I should write this so as to
never forget it.

Anaïs Nin (1903–1977)
French-born American writer

*R*ecording happiness made it last longer, we felt, and recording sorrow dramatized it and took away its bitterness; and often we settled some problem which beset us even while we wrote about it.

Dorothy Day (1897–1980)
American activist

People who keep journals live
life twice. Having written
something down gives you the
opportunity to go back to it
over and over, to remember
and relive the experience.

Jessamyn West (1907–1984)
American writer

Sometimes we need a
map of the past. It helps us
to understand the present, and
to plan the future.

Josephine Hart
20th-century Irish writer

To look backward for a while is to refresh the eye, to restore it, and to render it the more fit for its prime function of looking forward.

**Margaret Fairless Barber
(1869–1901)
English writer**

*I*t is a strangely pleasurable thing to read your own words from widely varying periods and phases of your life. You can hear not just how you thought but how you sounded at the moment you were thinking it. It's so much clearer and more specific than when your memory plays it back.

Merrill Markoe
20th-century American writer

I often reread old journals and
make notes to my former selves
in the margin.

Gail Godwin, b. 1937
American writer

I am writing these pages in
order to reread them in a year,
in thirty years—that will take
me back to my youth, like a
landscape you want
to see again and go back
to—you remembered it as
lovely, smiling, the leaves
all green. . . .

Gustave Flaubert (1821–1880)
French writer

Most people are conscious sometimes of strange and beautiful fancies swimming before their eyes: the pen is the wand to arrest, and the journal is the mirror to detain and fix them.

Robert Willmott (1809–1863)
English historian

We are drawn toward journals out of a craving for the authentic, for the uncensored word and thought.

Mark Rudman, b. 1948
American writer

Where I would like to discover facts, I find fancy. Where I would like to learn what I did, I learn only what I was thinking. They are loaded with opinion, moral thoughts, quick evaluations, youthful hopes and cares and sorrows. Occasionally, they manage to report something in exquisite honesty and accuracy.

E. B. White (1899–1985)
American writer

Journal writing is a voyage to
the interior.

Christina Baldwin, b. 1946
American writer

. . . diaries should be like a ripped or stained sloppy bathrobe you put on when you're alone, that you can be yourself in. Some are more like fancy bathrobes waiting for company. . . . Nothing I'd wear for just me and the cat.

Lyn Lifshin, b. 1942
American poet and writer

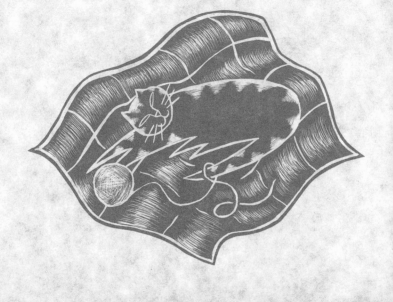

To write honestly and with all
our powers is the least we can
do, and the most.

Eudora Welty, b. 1909
American writer

*C*an you tell the truth in memoirs like these? I have tried to. But I am conscious that memory, blurred and disjointed by the passage of time, and brightened by the imagination, can lead one often to recount more fiction than fact.

William L. Shirer, b. 1904
American writer

One may lie to oneself, lie to
the world, lie to God, even,
but to one's pen one
cannot lie.

Willa Cather (1876–1947)
American writer

Perhaps these pages may never meet a human eye—and therefore no EXCESSIVE vanity can dictate them tho a feeling akin to SELF LOVE may have prompted my not unwilling pen.

**Elizabeth Barrett Browning
(1806–1861)
English poet**

. . . why the journal distresses
me, but also fascinates: I'm
required to use my own voice.
And record only the truth. But
not to record *all* the truth. There
have been many things I've
eliminated over the years . . .
or hinted at so slantwise no
one could guess. . . . Still,
what *is* recorded is always
true. At least at the time
it is recorded.

Joyce Carol Oates, b. 1938
American writer

*E*verybody reads my journal, but since I have been making sketches of character . . . I keep it under lock and key. . . . In my plain speaking and candour, what have I not said, intending no eye save mine to rest upon this page. The things I cannot tell exactly as they are, I do not intend to tell at all.

**Mary Bokin Chesnut
(1823–1886)
American writer**

$\mathcal{S}$ometimes what someone
chooses to write down is more
important than what they say.

Patricia MacLachlan, b. 1938
American writer

There is no greater delight than to be conscious of sincerity on self-examination.

Mencius (371–289 B.C.)
Chinese philosopher

One always runs the risk of creating a false impression when one sets out for the purest of motives—honesty and humility—to portray oneself "warts and all"; the warts have a habit of commandeering the artist's canvas.

Susan Howatch, b. 1940
English writer

Yes, the truth was crude sometimes, and she wanted to know it, to touch it and to let it touch her.

Elizabeth Cunningham, b. 1953
American writer

It's all right to twist the truth and lie with other people but don't do it with yourself, your secret self, or you are lost.

James Clavell, b. 1925
Australian-born American
writer

If I should write an honest
diary, what should I say?
Alas, that life has halfness,
shallowness. I have almost
completed thirty-nine years,
and I have not adjusted my
relation to my fellows on the
planet, or to my own work.
Always too young or too old,
I do not justify myself; how can
I satisfy others?

**Ralph Waldo Emerson
(1803–1882)
American writer and poet**

I want to write, but more than that, I want to bring out all kinds of things that lie buried deep in my heart.

Anne Frank (1929–1945)
Dutch diarist

The secret thoughts of a man run over all things, holy, profane, clean, obscene, grave and light, without shame or blame.

**Thomas Hobbes (1588–1679)
English philosopher**

In describing my experience I am recording not what happened or what exists but how I perceive it. In so doing I define myself. As I create my diary I create myself.

Tristine Rainer
20th-century American
educator and writer

$\mathcal{C}$reating oneself and explaining oneself proceed side by side, inseparably. Temperament *is* the act of commenting on itself.

Richard Powers, b. 1957
American writer

We are so many selves. . . .
the person we were last year,
wanted to be yesterday, tried
to become in one job or in
one winter, in one love affair
or in one house where even
now, we can close our eyes
and smell the rooms.

Gloria Steinem, b. 1934
American writer and editor

It makes me laugh to read over this diary. It's so full of contradictions, and one would think I was such an unhappy woman. Yet is there a happier woman than I?

Sophie Tolstoy (1844–1919)
Russian diarist

The chief utility of the *journal intime* is to restore the integrity of the mind and the equilibrium of the conscience, that is, inner health.

H. F. Amiel (1821–1881)
French writer

I write to bring back what is gone, to relive what is lost, to make a mosaic out of fragments.

Minfong Ho, b. 1951
Burmese-born American writer

You write by sitting down and writing. There's no particular time or place—you suit yourself, your nature.

Bernard Malamud
(1914–1986)
American writer

The perfect place for a writer is in the hideous roar of a city, with men making a new road under his window in competition with a barrel organ, and on the mat a man waiting for the rent.

**Henry Vollam Morton
(1892–1979)
English writer**

I sit in bed with a big breakfast
and then I write. I like that.

Katharine Hepburn, b. 1909
American actress

*W*riting is an escape from a world that crowds me.
I like being alone in a room.
It's almost always a form of meditation—an investigation of my own life.

Neil Simon, b. 1927
American dramatist

I write every morning as soon after the first light as possible. There is no one to disturb you and it is cool or cold and you . . . warm as you write.

Ernest Hemingway
(1899–1961)
American writer

If you're trying to write, you
have to let your attention drop.
You can't maintain an interest
in anything else.

Barbara Tuchman, b. 1912
American historian

To me . . . writing is addictive.
If I don't get to write three or
four times a week, I start
getting very angry with
people, very annoyed.

Laurence Yep, b. 1948
Chinese-American writer

*O*ne ought to write only when one leaves a piece of one's flesh in the inkpot each time one dips one's pen.

**Leo Nikolayevich Tolstoy
(1828–1910)
Russian philosopher and writer**

I aim to set down in this journal all that happens to us on this trip. I shall do it as truly and faithfully as I can. . . .

Barbara Brenner, b. 1925
American writer

Whether you buy a little
leather travel book you can
toss into your pocket or purse
or a blank book, it is fun to
record each trip. Each of us,
wherever we live, has to find
our own blank book that will
inspire travel entries.

Alexandra Stoddard
20th-century American writer

$\mathcal{D}$on't tear up the page
and start over when you write
a bad line. . . .

Garrison Keillor, b. 1942
American writer

One truth discovered, one pang of regret at not being able to express it, is better than all the fluency and flippancy in the world.

William Hazlitt (1778–1830)
English writer

A diary need not be
a dreary chronicle of one's
movements; it should aim
rather at giving a salient
account of some particular
episode, a walk, a book,
a conversation.

A. C. Benson (1862–1925)
English writer and editor

. . . though the thoughts may
not be very profound, nor the
remarks very lively and
ingenious, nor the narrative of
exceeding interest, still the
exercise is, I think, calculated
to make the writer wiser and
perhaps better.

**Charles C. F. Greville
(1794–1865)
English diarist**

For any writer who wants to keep a journal, remember to be alive to everything, not just to what you're feeling, but also to your pets, to flowers, to what you are reading.

May Sarton (1912–1985)
Belgian-born American writer
and poet

To one who has enjoyed the full life of any scene, of any hour, what thoughts can be recorded about it seem like the commas and semicolons in the paragraph—mere stops.

Margaret Fuller (1810–1850)
American writer, editor,
and poet

There are sounds to seasons.
There are sounds to places,
and there are sounds to every
time in one's life.

Alison Wyrley Birch, b. 1922
American writer

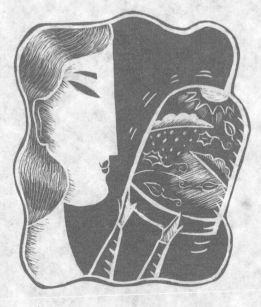

. . . it's often on days when I
thought nothing happened that
I'll start writing and go on for
pages, a single sound or sight
recalled from the afternoon
suddenly loosing a chain
of thoughts.

Thomas Mallon, b. 1951
American educator and writer

An incurable itch for scribbling
takes possession of many
and grows inveterate in their
insane hearts.

Juvenal (55–60 A.D.)
Roman poet and satirist

Go into yourself. Search for the reason that bids you write, find out whether it is spreading out its roots in the deepest place of your heart.

**Rainer Maria Rilke
(1875–1926)
German poet**

A diary should simply be.

Gertrude Stein (1874–1946)
American writer

A diary may give us a picture of a man or a picture of an age. The writer may turn his gaze inward, hardly troubling to record outward events . . . he may paint for us his heart and secret mind. If he does this, it does not matter who he was and when or where he lived; he has given us a document of human interest.

J. B. Priestley (1894–1984)
English writer

I suppose journal keeping is a
kind of talking to oneself.

Jessamyn West (1907–1984)
American writer

$\mathcal{W}$riting, when properly managed . . . is but a different name for conversation.

Laurence Stern (1713–1768)
English cleric and writer

I've decided to keep up this
habit of writing at night. . . .
It's a relief, like talking to an
adult in the evening. Of
course, there's no response
from a blank page. Still, it
feels as if there were.

Marilyn French, b. 1929
American writer

Don't you think sometimes that memories are like old friends? You can summon them up much as you would reach for a telephone. They come into your consciousness and comfort you.

John Katzenback, b. 1950
American writer

I must write it all out, at any
cost. Writing is thinking. It is
more than living, for it is being
conscious of living.

**Anne Morrow Lindbergh,
b. 1906
American writer and poet**

*I*t is as if the life lived has not been lived until it is set down in this unconscious sequence of words.

Edna O'Brien, b. 1932
Irish writer

Like so much in her life, filling
the diary had become an act of
self-preservation. Someday,
someone would read her journal
and know. . . .

William Martin, b. 1950
American writer

That is the magic of language:
every word waits to come true.
Description gives way to
postulate, is refined by
experiment into singing
celebration.

**Richard Powers, b. 1957
American writer**

$\mathcal{W}$e traveled from the past back into the present, and found the two in many ways identical. Old foolishness is not improved with age, nor are ancient hostilities dignified by the fact that they happened long ago.

Peter Ustinov, b. 1921
English actor, playwright,
and writer

. . . as long as there is memory, it does help us broaden our lives and our pleasures and connect us with a constantly filling past.

Nat Eek, b. 1927
American educator and writer

What good is this journal?
I cling to these pages as to
something fixed among so
many fugitive things.

André Gide (1869–1951)
French writer

I never travel without my diary. One should always have something sensational to read in the train.

Oscar Wilde (1854–1900)
Irish poet and playwright

Writing a journal implies that
one has ceased to think of the
future and has decided to live
wholly in the present. . . .
Writing a journal means that
facing your ocean you are
afraid to swim across it,
so you attempt to drink it
drop by drop.

George Sand (1804–1876)
French writer

"The horror of that moment,"
the King went on, "I shall
never, never forget!"
"You will, though," the Queen
said, "if you don't make a
memorandum of it."

**Lewis Carroll (1832–1898)
English mathematician
and writer**

What fun it is to generalize in the privacy of a notebook. It is as I imagine waltzing on ice might be. A great delicious sweep in one direction, taking you your full strength, and then with no trouble at all an equally delicious sweep in the opposite direction.

Florida Scott-Maxwell
(1884–1979)
American writer
and playwright

Life piles up so fast that I have no time to write out the equally fast rising mound of reflections, which I always mark down as they rise to be inserted here.

Virginia Woolf (1882-1941)
English writer

It is hard to write about the life
one is actually living.

Robert Finch
20th-century American editor

Pouring out one's insides
may sound easy but it comes
hard—especially when
expressing personal feelings—
in truth.

Pearl Bailey (1918–1990)
American entertainer
and writer

It is not easy to write in a
journal what interests us at any
time, because to write it is not
what interests us.

**Henry David Thoreau
(1817–1862)
American writer**

*Y*ou can only write what you need to write.

P. D. James, b. 1920
English writer

A day is like a whole life.
You start out doing one thing,
but end up doing something
else, plan to run an errand, but
never get there. . . . And at
the end of your life, your
whole existence has that same
haphazard quality, too. Your
whole life has the same shape
as a single day.

Michael Crichton, b. 1942
American writer

*B*ut that's the adventure
. . . . that I don't know what's
around the corner or beyond
the next rise. I don't need to
be told, just encouraged to go
on and find out for myself.

Elizabeth Cunningham, b. 1953
American writer

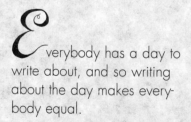

$\mathcal{E}$verybody has a day to
write about, and so writing
about the day makes everybody equal.

William Melvin Kelley
20th-century American writer

Every life contains within it a
potential for clarification.

Peter Hoeg, b. 1957
Danish writer

Everybody is original, if he
tells the truth, if he speaks from
himself. . . . Consequently, if
you speak or write from
yourself you cannot help
being original.

**Brenda Ueland (1891–1985)
American educator, editor,
and writer**

Each discrete life examines and explains everything it touches in a constant exchange of mutual defining and reshaping. By living, we become our times' biographer.

Richard Powers, b. 1957
American writer

. . . even the simplest events
grow mossy with the passage
of years.

Larry McMurtry, b. 1936
American writer

*I*f she retains a fragment of dream, it will blow away unless she can chronologize it and put it into words.

Austin Wright, b. 1922
American writer

It is a strange experience
reading your own diary forty
or fifty years after you've
written it. . . . Characters
keep appearing whose very
existence I had forgotten. . . .
I can foresee their destinies;
their futures are laid out, all
the crisscrossed lines where
my life intersected theirs. It is
somehow terrible to become
possessed, suddenly, of all that
foresight, a pointillism of time.

S. N. Behrman (1893–1937)
American writer

. . . nothing in the past stays
fixed forever; as we grow and
change the past changes;
when I look back I did not
always find exactly what
I had expected. . . .

May Sarton (1912–1985)
Belgian-born American writer
and poet

It might be of great profit to me; and now that I am older, that I have more time, that the labour of writing is less onerous to me, and I can work more at my leisure, I ought to endeavor to keep, to a certain extent, a record of passing impressions, of all that comes, that goes, that I see, and feel, and observe. To catch and keep something of life—that's what I mean.

Henry James (1811–1882)
American writer

And now, O my journal! art thou not highly dignified? Shalt thou not flourish tenfold?

**James Boswell (1740–1795)
Scottish writer**

Words and magic were in
the beginning one and the
same thing, and even today
words contain much of their
magical power.

**Sigmund Freud (1856–1939)
Austrian psychoanalyst**

Writing is a form of therapy;
sometimes I wonder how all
those who do not write,
compose or paint can manage
to escape the madness, the
melancholia, the panic fear
which is inherent in a
human situation.

Graham Greene, b. 1904
British writer

I write to understand.

Eli Wiesel, b. 1928
Romanian-born
American writer

*T*hat's it—the only way to
cure the pains . . . the private
journal. . . . Trust us there,
where we begin to
trust ourselves.

**Hortense Calisher, b. 1911
American writer**

*W*hatever is bothering you, write it down in a book. Close the book, and a year later you'll open it up and say, "Big deal."

Joan Rivers, b. 1933
American entertainer

There it is on paper, you say,
plainly to be read, so it
couldn't have been so
unendurable.

Edna Ferber (1887–1968)
American writer

. . . and if I have not written
words upon paper as I should
like to have done, I have
written large upon the page of
life that was left open for me.

Louis L'Amour (1908–1988)
American writer